WE LOVE YOU
TRUDY

By Jerry Marcus

tempo
books

GROSSET & DUNLAP
A FILMWAYS COMPANY
Publishers • New York

To Honey

WE LOVE YOU
TRUDY

By Jerry Marcus

"Jerry Marcus has a rare ability to get the most fun out of life with the least strokes of the pen. I love you, Trudy."

Mort Walker
Creator of Beetle Bailey and Hi and Lois

"The reason I like TRUDY as a cartoon panel is simply that I like the characters themselves. . . . And, of course, I like Jerry Marcus because he has always been a real professional."

Charles M. Schulz
Creator of Peanuts

"Good morning, pots—good morning, pans—here we go again."

"Start the pancakes! He just moved his pinky!"

"WAKE UP! THE WORLD IS YOUR OYSTER! Except, of course, for the months without an 'R' in them!"

"And whom, pray, am I saying good morning to —
Doctor Jekyll or Mr. Hyde?"

"Mirror, mirror on the wall, who is the fairest one of all — him or me?"

"I know I told you I like my oatmeal thick..."

"Before you come home tonight, pick up a box of handkerchiefs and a nice necktie and a card from me to you — today's your birthday."

" 'Scrambled eggs... soft-boiled eggs... fried eggs!'
Decisions... decisions... decisions..."

"Just practicing — no blade."

"You've tidied up your room and now you're doing your homework — just what the heck are you up to?"

"Don't be silly — if Mother were mad at you, would she be smiling?"

"Just think, Mom — school will be out soon and we'll have the WHOLE summer together!"

"Listen, I'm probably the best certified accountant in town and I can't figure my wife out!"

"Your wife's been in a bad mood all day — see what YOU can do with her!"

"Go ahead — now ask ME what kind of day _I_ had!"

"No, I don't think President Carter would mind the fuel we'll be using to heat the water for your bath."

"Look at him — it's hard to believe that quiet rosy-cheeked little boy, just a few hours ago, gave me a case of the screaming meemies!"

"If the sirloin steak tastes funny, it's because it's really hamburger SHAPED like a sirloin."

"I'm going to do the dishes, and I want to see two goldfish in that bowl when I get back."

"WELL, IF YOU'RE <u>REALLY</u> DRESSING TO PLEASE ME, YOU'LL DO IT <u>FASTER!</u>"

"Ted! Listen! He's playing our song!"

"Be right with you, Mom — I'm just waiting for my gum to come around again!"

"Well, what do you think — do we put him out tonight?"

"For a guy who's ninety percent water → you're not bad lookin' at all!"

"Very funny."

"Let's see now, I'll be away at Mother's for three days..."

"I started out knitting you a pair of socks. Then I said 'what the heck'!"

"Washday."

"You're gonna laugh when you hear this, Trudy —
seems I got it all wrong — we're having dinner at
THEIR house tonight!"

"Have I thanked you for your efforts through the years in preventing the sofa cushions from fading?"

"A word with Fatkat, please."

"If you're having the boys over for poker tonight, we might as well make the house presentable. You can take down the storm windows, paint the kitchen chairs, fix the..."

"Is that you, Ted? How was your poker game?"

"So there I sat, holding four kings — now get this — Dick Wingert is holding a full house, aces high — Bill Yates is holding a straight flush — now the fun begins..."

"Can you ask the doctor to bring the shots out here?"

"Oh, yes, don't forget Rodney's dog food!"

"Listen, Rodney! There it is again! There's something in the cellar!"

"I'll be back in an hour, Trudy — gonna get a hair-cut!"

"Grandma, how much was fourteen times eight in the old days?"

"It is one minute after twelve — guess what kid has a birthday today!"

"CUT! CUT! Trudy, you're bringing the cake in too fast — and, kids - laugh it up! NOW LET'S TRY IT AGAIN!"

"Don't worry about 'em falling down, Julius — I've been around a lot longer'n you, an' none of 'em ever fell on me."

"I'm not sure, but I don't think planned parenthood means you get to pick your own parents."

" 'Getting away from it all' — who's getting away from
it all? We're taking it ALL with us!"

"Dad! Look at me! Dad?"

"I haven't had so much fun since the last time I cleaned my oven!"

"It's a strike, all right — wrong alley — but you got a strike!"

"The bumper jack? Is that the metal thing I use as a doorstop in my laundry room?"

"Now, wasn't that a great vacation, Trudy? You un-pack, I'll be back in a couple of hours."

"I told her — I don't mind you working for Women's Lib as long as you're home in time to defrost my TV dinner."

"BATTLE STATIONS, EVERYONE!"

"Don't you DARE take another step until I get the sand out of the cuffs of your pants!"

"That's wonderful, Ted! Now wait till you see what <u>I</u> got in the low seventies!"

"I've forgotten what the commercial called it -- but when you spray it on, suddenly you're coming out of a blue lagoon on to the beach of a tropical isle!"

"Ted, remember you've got a dental appointment in the morning!"

"Oh, dear, the roast STILL isn't ready — better make them some more drinks!"

"You better get up and go see why the bathroom faucet isn't dripping."

"I made some oatmeal for breakfast, Mom — do you want one lump or two?"

"I'm off to the movies, Trudy — I'll pick you up here on the way home!"

"Mrs. Nozie thinks my stew needs more salt, and if it tastes right she'll stay for dinner."

"Where can I contact you when I change my mind?"

"Remember, Trudy — you're not to repeat this to anyone except Maryann Bogley, Sue Michaud, Irene Kampen, Nellie Farbush..."

"I wouldn't say anything about her unless I could say something good — and boy, is this GOOD!"

"Oh, I know my Charlie is shiftless, bad tempered, stubborn, stingy, thoughtless, crude — but then I think — no man is perfect."

"Well, I'll be—YOU'RE an up and downsie—I always thought you were a side-to-side brusher!"

"I always meant to ask you, what attracted you to me
— was it may sex appeal, brains, glamour...?"

"Oh, I forgot to tell you — Stanley Klar called and asked if you'd go bowling with him last Monday night."

"Might as well bring your fish in, too, Ed — Trudy can
clean 'em all at the same time."

"Of course it's complicated — would you trust an insurance policy you could understand?"

"On your mark — get ready — get set…"

"I've read three books on dieting this month, and I've decided to give up reading."

"Trudy, there are some friends of mine I'd like you to
meet — I'm sending them over to your place!"

"After all, dear, we knew it was just a matter of time."

"... Then, after breakfast, I was gonna do the dishes
and vacuum — and then I thought, 'What the heck.' "

"Remember, every cloud has a silver lining! It's always darkest before the dawn! It's a great big wonderful world! Laugh and the world laughs with you!..."

"I didn't say the meat was tough — all I said was I can't slice the gravy."

"They heard a weird noise downstairs!"

"Ted, you better get home right away — I've got another mouse trapped in the basement!"

"I'll bet Rod Carew's mother doesn't make him take a bath after he's gone five for six!"

"Well, the doctor said according to my weight I should be eight feet, seven and one-half-inches tall."

"Can I speak to you ALONE, Trudy?"

"He's getting too much sleep."

"Good luck."

"Now take it easy — it's just a little jacket for Fatkat."

"Mirror, mirror, on the wall, who stretches a food dollar farthest of them all?"

"I must say, you have a nice voice for a recording."

"Remember, Mom — it may look like a mess to you,
but I know just where everything is!"

"Very funny, Mr. Pipkin — now, for the last time, can I see your mussels?"

"I got four at this end — how many do you have, Julius?"

"Do you want mother to warm up the TV set before she leaves?"

"I'll tell you what money can't buy nowadays — the same stuff it bought last week!"

"Do you have any low-calorie plant food for fat plants?"

"Somehow, that's not the kind of watchdog I expected him to turn out to be."

"NOW, GET OUT THERE AND MAKE WAVES!"

"I'm glad to see the excitement hasn't gone out of your marriage."

"Be out of the tub in a minute, Mom—just finishing up!"

"Ted, the doctor wants you to come to the phone so he can hear your 'wheeze'!"

"Grandma, how old would a person be today if they were born in 1910?"

"Man or woman?"

"Look, all I want is a cup of coffee and I don't see why I should have to hand wrestle you for it."

"Mom, when did you first suspect that I wasn't a gifted child?"

"Some parents believe that arguing in front of children is bad. As a kid, I think it's healthy.. I SAID, some parents believe..."

"You here to referee the fight, Grandma?"

"Now, you EAT that or I'll give it to Daddy!"

"What do you see? What's out there?"

"The question is, sweetie — can the world face YOU this morning?"

"If his temperature should go up to 102 again -- SELL!
— er, I mean, er, give him two of these pills."

"All right — where is he?"

"Our game was called on account of broken glass."

"Sure, it's easy for you to say... you're not afraid of the lightning and thunder because you've got Mom!"

"Good morning, World — I'm up!"

"Ted, have you seen my false eyelashes?"

"... And stop complaining about the drinks and the food — this is OUR party, remember?"

·∽· the ·∽·
Fatkat
Glossary

cat-sup

cat-call

cat-ty

cat-astrophe!

cat-ercornered

cat-walk

cat-a-comb

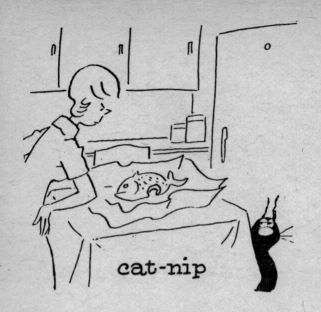

cat-nip

cat-fish

cat-a-lyst

cat-a-log

THEY WERE THE FIRST CATS
IN THE COLOSSEUM

MY ANCESTORS LANDED
ON PLYMOUTH ROCK!

THEY FLEW WITH
ALL THE GREAT WITCHES!

THEY SAILED AROUND THE HORN!

THEY SIGNED THE DECLARATION
OF INDEPENDENCE!